W9-ABQ-901

O, star of wonder, star of might,
Star with royal beauty bright,
Westward leading, still proceeding,
Guide us to the perfect Light.

STAR OF WONDER

STAR OF

McGRAW-HILL BOOK COMPANY, INC., NEW YOR

WONDER

ROBERT R. COLES
CHAIRMAN, THE HAYDEN PLANETARIUM
AND
FRANCES FROST

PICTURES BY **PAUL GALDONE**

TORONTO LONDON

5346

Contents

Chapter 1

THE DAY BEFORE CHRISTMAS

It was the day before Christmas. The sky outside the windows was a soft dull gray. When Dad came home for lunch he told David and Jean that the air smelled as if it were going to snow. The children were very excited.

After lunch they decorated their tree. David and Jean took care of the lower branches, which they could reach, while Mother and Dad did the upper boughs. They all sang carols together while they hung the shining blue and red and green and silver balls on the tall fragrant spruce. Then Mother looped the tinsel and Dad helped her. David and

Jean proudly draped the popcorn and cranberry ropes they had strung yesterday afternoon. They all flung tinfoil icicles at the tree until the green branches dripped with glitter.

Dad steadied the stepladder and Jean picked the great golden star from the box.

"May I please put the Christmas Star on top of the tree?" she asked.

"It's my turn this year," said David, "but you go ahead." Then he added thoughtfully, "I wonder what the Christmas Star was."

"Why, it was a special star that God put in the sky for the shepherds and the Wise Men to follow so they could find the Little Lord Jesus," said Jean.

"Well, I know there was a star . . . but how did it get there?"

"For goodness' sake," Jean said, "no wonder Mother calls you a human question mark."

"If you're going to be a scientist, you have to ask questions about everything. My teacher says so."

"Speaking of the Christmas Star," said Dad, his eyes twinkling, "I read in the paper that there is a Christmas Show being given at the Planetarium now. It's all about the Star of Bethlehem. It might help you to answer this very question. Would you like to go and see it?"

"Oh, yes, Dad!" cried David. He and Jean had been to the Planetarium before and had seen the heavens and stars shown on the great curved ceiling. "I'd like to go," he said.

"Oh, yes, let's!" said Jean.

"I'll tell you what," said Mother with a smile. "Let's leave our own star until later. I'll take you to the Planetarium. I have to call on a friend of mine near there. You may go see the Show, and I'll meet you afterward."

"That's a fine idea," said Dad. "I'll put our star on the mantelpiece until you get back and leave the stepladder here. Scoot and get your coats."

"Oh, boy!" said David. "The Planetarium sure is wonderful." He looked scornfully at his little sister. "Too bad girls aren't better scientists."

"I don't care!" said Jean stoutly. "I know what I know, that's what I know!"

Chapter 2

IN THE THEATER OF THE STARS

David and Jean and Mother left the bus. The grassy lawns around the Planetarium were brown and dry. The pale green dome of the Planetarium rose above the bare boughs of the trees. David sniffed to see if he could smell snow coming, but all he could smell was chilly air.

In the Planetarium lobby, Mother told David and Jean she would meet them here when the program was over.

It was nearly time for the Christmas Show to begin upstairs. In the distance, the children could hear carols being played.

"Let's hurry!" said David.

They walked into the dim rose-and-blue light that filled the great dome of the Planetarium. They found seats and watched other children and grownups crowding eagerly into the great round hall.

Ahead of them gleamed a big fantastic machine which was a star projector. Around the horizon of the room was pictured the outline of the city's towering skyline.

David knew that the big projector was really a super magic lantern which could throw great pictures of the sky on the dome.

The exit doors were closed and the rose-and-blue light faded into darkness. Somewhere a tinkling music box was playing Christmas music. David held his breath. Gently the music clinked to a stop.

Suddenly the children were gazing at the night sky filled with millions of stars.

"Oh-h!" whispered Jean with awe and delight.

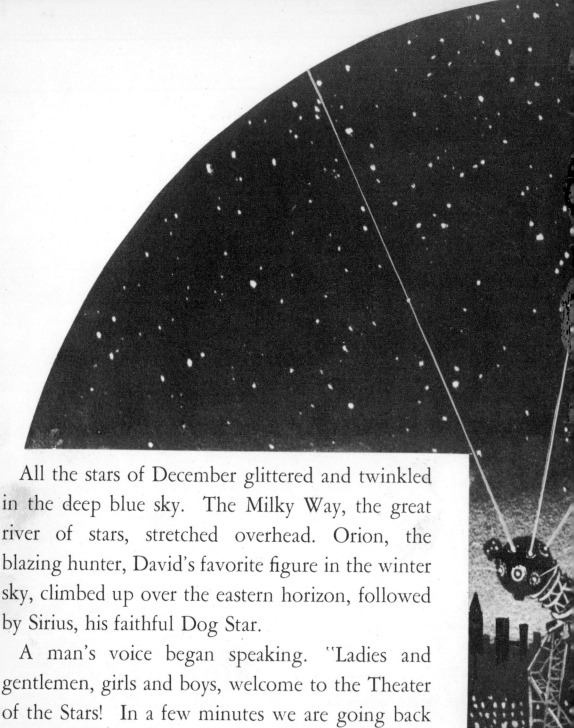

All the stars of December glittered and twinkled in the deep blue sky. The Milky Way, the great river of stars, stretched overhead. Orion, the blazing hunter, David's favorite figure in the winter sky, climbed up over the eastern horizon, followed by Sirius, his faithful Dog Star.

A man's voice began speaking. "Ladies and gentlemen, girls and boys, welcome to the Theater of the Stars! In a few minutes we are going back through time to the night when Christ was born. The big machine that you see in front of you is a Zeiss Projector. It will show you the heavens as they were over Bethlehem nearly twenty centuries ago."

"Gosh," David murmured to Jean, "I always wondered what it was like back then!"

"I know what it was like," she whispered back. "The shepherds were watching their flocks—"

"Sh-h!" David said.

"Tonight is the night before Christmas," said the speaker, "and I shall be your guide back through the many centuries to the first Christmastime. Christmas means many things to many people. But now we are most interested in the story of the star that led the Wise Men to Bethlehem when Jesus was born."

David smiled at Jean and lifted his eyes to the sky once more.

Chapter 3

WHAT WAS THE CHRISTMAS STAR ?

Music began again, playing "Silent Night." Across the stars and the outline of the city's towers, snow began to fall slowly at first and then faster. The snow storm blotted out the high roof tops and the sky.

"The projector," said the speaker, "is taking us back across the bridge of years to the first Christmas."

The snow storm gradually ceased, and then the sky was wide and clear. Now around the walls of the Planetarium the horizon of city towers had changed to the hills of Galilee.

The stars David had seen before were in different positions in the sky and there were some strange stars that he didn't know.

The low starlit hills were covered with vines and olive trees. The olive trees had gray bark and their leaves were smooth and thick, grayish green above and white underneath. David looked around at the rolling hills and thought of how lonely it must have been for the shepherds who watched their flocks there thousands of years ago.

Suddenly in front of David and Jean was a picture
of the Kings, the Magi, on their camels. They were
carrying their gifts of gold, frankincense, and myrrh
and searching across the hills for a sign of the Christ
Child. They seemed to be gazing toward the

heavens, but David couldn't discover which star they were looking at.

He and Jean were sitting on the edges of their seats, tense with excitement.

"Where's the Christmas Star?" Jean asked.

"Wait," said David, "they'll find it."

The picture on the dome faded and there was only the vast sky filled with splendid stars. The children sighed and slid back in their seats.

The speaker said that many people believe that the Star of Bethlehem was a miracle seen by the Wise Men.

But there are many other people who believe that the Star was perfectly visible to everyone and that scientists can explain what was happening in the sky at the time when Christ was born.

Astronomers have been interested for many years in figuring out which stars and planets were visible at that time. They have tried to find a star which the Wise Men might have followed.

They have several different ideas as to what the Christmas Star may have been. We are going to explore these now.

Chapter 4

WAS IT A METEOR ?

In ancient times the shepherds who tended their flocks watched the passage of the stars across the night sky. They told the time of year by the rising of some stars and the sinking of others. They gave the names of animals to great shapes they imagined they saw the stars make—the Ram, the Bull, the Big and Little Bears, the Lion, the Dog.

And watching the heavens night after night, they would certainly have noticed anything unusual that happened there.

The Wise Men, the Magi, also were watchers of the skies. They lived in the open country of Persia. They studied the heavens and used the stars as beacons to guide them through the night. They believed, too, that there would come a sign in the sky that would announce the birth of a new King.

But what did they see?

Some astronomers think they saw a very brilliant meteor, or falling star. A meteor is not really a star. It is a solid chunk of matter from outer space. When a meteor enters the air around the earth at a terrific speed, it is heated by friction until it glows. As it shoots through space, it leaves a trail of light behind it.

David gulped. At that exact moment, across the sky of the Planetarium, a blazing meteor flashed, and then its green-white trail died out. "Wow!" he said.

Jean gazed open-mouthed at the starry sky. Then she said sorrowfully, "It's all gone."

"Now and then," said the speaker, "meteors are bright enough to light up the countryside for miles around. But they never stay in sight very long.

And a meteor couldn't be followed for several nights, as the Wise Men followed the Star of Bethlehem."

"So it probably wasn't a meteor," David murmured to his little sister.

Chapter 5

WAS IT A COMET ?

Some astronomers have suggested that the Christmas Star might have been a comet.

Nothing startled our ancestors more than the unexpected appearance in the heavens of those peculiar objects with bright heads and streaming tails which we call comets. The word "comet" comes from a Greek word which means "long-haired."

Even after men first began to understand the movements of the sun and the planets they thought that comets were wanderers which prowled about the sky doing evil.

No one is sure where comets come from or where they go. But scientists no longer believe the old superstitions that they cause plagues and wars and the murders of kings.

The center of the comet looks like a star. It is thought to be made up of solid particles. The tail of a comet is made up of gas and cosmic dust, which is forced backward as the comet approaches the sun. As the comet leaves the sun, its tail begins to get in front of its head. Some comets have had two, four, six, or even nine tails.

Sometimes comets seem to come out of space, to circle the sun, and then travel away again, never to return. Others seem to be a regular part of our solar system. And a comet may be visible from a few days to several months.

One very famous comet is called Halley's comet. It appears from time to time. It was last seen in 1910. It will return again around 1986.

"Some scientists," said the Planetarium speaker, "think the Magi saw a comet whose head pointed toward the horizon and led them to the Christ Child, like a great finger in the heavens.

"But there is no certain record that a comet appeared around the time Christ was born."

"Oh, look, David!" gasped Jean.

A great ball of light with a long streaming tail moved slowly across the Planetarium sky and pointed toward the southwest hills.

"Gosh!" he said. "I hope we live long enough to see Halley's comet!"

Slowly the comet sank behind the hills, drawing its brilliant tail after it.

"Now that's gone, too!" wailed Jean.

"Never mind," said David. "That probably wasn't the Christmas Star, either."

Chapter 6

WAS IT A NEW STAR ?

"In the year 1604," said the speaker, "the famous German astronomer Johannes Kepler saw a nova, or new star. He suggested that it might have been such a new star that was seen by the Magi."

New stars are not really new. They have always been in the heavens but they are usually too dim to be seen with the naked eye.

Suddenly, for some reason, they flare up to startling brightness. This is because there is a terrific outward rush of energy and glowing gases, like an explosion within the star. Then gradually the star fades from sight once more.

The speaker explained, "Since the light of a new star grows dim after a few weeks or months, a nova might have been the sign which the Wise Men watched in the heavens. It would have looked like this."

In the Planetarium sky, a faint star appeared near the Milky Way. It suddenly began to expand and to grow swiftly to great golden brilliance.

"Oh, my, that's pretty!" Jean sighed.

The new star glowed very brightly for several minutes. Then it began to grow dim again until it was once more nearly invisible, a small speck in the great sweep of the stars. Then it was gone.

"I wish they wouldn't all keep disappearing!" Jean mourned.

"Cheer up," David consoled her. "There's more coming."

Chapter 7

THREE PLANETS

The astronomers have still other ideas as to what might have been the Christmas Star.

During the time when Jesus was born, the three great planets, Jupiter, Saturn, and Mars, appeared together in the *same part* of the sky.

An astonishing thing happened. As they moved around the sun the giant planet Jupiter passed Saturn three times!

This was something the Magi could not possibly have seen before. The passing of one planet by another is called a conjunction. It was of great importance to the astronomers of that time. And since the Magi were watching for a sign in the sky, this conjunction of Jupiter and Saturn would have had a very special meaning for them.

It could have meant the sign heralding the birth of a new King!

And early the next year, the red planet, Mars, which had been a distance to the west of Jupiter and Saturn, moved into the picture and joined them to form a triangle.

Jean grabbed David's hand. "Look!" she breathed.

Low above the southwest hills, in the deep blue Planetarium sky, blazed Jupiter and Saturn.   Then Mars, burning red, shot up from the west and joined them to make a perfect triangle.

The speaker continued, "Today some astronomers think that it could have been this coming together of Jupiter and Saturn and Mars that attracted the Magi and was interpreted by them as the sign for which they were searching."

David took a deep breath.   He tightened his hand on Jean's.

Scientists have pointed out that this was not a single star. But then many objects in the sky called stars are not really stars at all. This arrangement of the planets was, however, a sign and a remarkable one.

Suddenly on the Planetarium dome appeared a marvelous picture—the manger at Bethlehem. It was so real that it seemed to Jean she could almost reach out and touch the Little Lord Jesus.

"There He is!" she cried.

From the three planets a bright beam of light pointed downward to the manger where the Child lay, and music played "O Little Town of Bethlehem."

The speaker said, "The Christmas Star might have been a meteor, or a comet, or a new star, or the three planets, Jupiter, Saturn, and Mars. Or it could have been a miracle that the Kings saw.

"The naming of the Star is not important. The really important thing is the *meaning* of the Star.

"Its radiance, which led the Magi to the humble birthplace of Jesus nearly two thousand years ago, has shone through the centuries. It shines on this Christmas Eve with its great message of

PEACE
ON EARTH
GOOD WILL
TO MEN

Chapter 8

THE CHRISTMAS STAR
IS IN MY HEART

Snow began to fall softly across the Planetarium sky. The big flakes covered the sky and hid the Christmas Star. David and Jean smiled at each other without saying a word. They didn't have to.

Slowly the big round room grew rose and blue again and the Show was over.

David helped Jean with her coat and hauled his own on. He took her hand.

They went downstairs as fast as they could. In the lobby there was Mother, smiling, waiting for them. They hurled themselves at her.

"Well, did you find out how the Christmas Star got there?"

"Oh, yes, we did!" David answered with excitement. "It could have been a meteor, or a new star, or a comet, or the way three planets looked."

Jean interrupted, "But it did shine for the Wise Men," she said.

"The important thing," said Mother, "is that it still shines on our Christmas trees and its message is in our hearts all year. Look outdoors," she added, laughing and hugging them.

David looked and saw great flakes coming down as heavily as those in the Planetarium. "Wow!" he shouted. "It's snowing for Christmas!"

"I bet the sky snowed on purpose just for the Little Lord Jesus!" exclaimed Jean.

"Let's hurry up," David urged. "I can't wait to get home and finish that tree." He began to sing, at the top of his voice, "We Three Kings of Orient Are!"

We three kings of Orient are,
Bearing gifts we traverse afar,
Field and fountain, moor and mountain,
Following yonder star.